PIANO • VOCAL • GUITAR

Barbra Streisand   The Broadway Album

HAL LEONARD PUBLISHING CORPORATION

Home Office: **National Sales Office:**
960 East Mark Street   8112 West Bluemound Road
Winona MN 55987   Milwaukee WI 53213

Notes by Alan & Marilyn Bergman

PUTTING IT TOGETHER

From Stephen Sondheim and *Sunday In The Park With George* come these dazzling observations on the eternal conflict between art and commerce. It is interesting to compare the original lyrics to these revised by Sondheim especially for this album.

IF I LOVED YOU

In 1943, Rodgers and Hammerstein introduced a new form of musical and ballet theater in the Pulitzer Prize-winning *Oklahoma*. Two years later came *Carousel*, continuing their innovative integration of music, lyrics and dance to tell the story. It contained one of the most unique love songs: "If I Loved You."

SOMETHING'S COMING

In *West Side Story*, the elements of music, lyrics, dance and dialogue are fused seamlessly. All of equal importance. The naturalistic choreography of Jerome Robbins, the modern retelling of *Romeo And Juliet* by Arthur Laurents, the wonderfully theatrical music of composer Leonard Bernstein and a young lyricist whose first show this was, Stephen Sondheim. From the world of the ghetto and gangs and interracial violence, Bernstein and Sondheim created a score as poetic as it is muscular, as hopeful as it is dark—with songs like "Something's Coming," which sounds as fresh today as when it was written—over 28 years ago.

NOT WHILE I'M AROUND

Not enough has been said about Sondheim, the composer. Perhaps it's because he's such a great lyric writer! But his music is always surprising, elegant and uncompromising.

Barbra sings, with breathtaking purity, this deceptively simple jewel of a song from *Sweeney Todd*.

BEING ALIVE

Company was, in the words of Sondheim, "an attempt to do a musical that had a story but no plot, with songs used as comment and counterpoint."

As such, it was a further development of the musical form. "Being Alive," the last song in the show, is about the best and the worst of a relationship.

I HAVE DREAMED/ WE KISS IN A SHADOW/ SOMETHING WONDERFUL

When Barbra was recording these songs from *The King And I*, she said, standing at the microphone after a take: "These songs feel so good to sing." Yes. Because they are so perfectly crafted. Rodgers and Hammerstein at their best.

SEND IN THE CLOWNS

This is probably the most prominent theater song of the decade, and deservedly so. (Every writer has a list of songs he wished he'd written. This is high up on ours.)

When Barbra began working on this song, she soon discovered that her favorite part musically was the bridge. She wanted to return to it. But, as an actress, it felt odd to repeat the lyric.

Once again, she took a deep breath before asking Steve if he would write an additional lyric for the second bridge. Once again, he said yes.

As lyricists we can appreciate how difficult it is for a writer to take a fresh look at something he wrote some 12 years before. But he did, without disturbing the subtlety, the obliqueness, the magic of the song.

There was just one more thing. Approaching the song as a scene, Barbra found that for her the strongest dramatic statement with which to end was, "Don't bother—they're here." Did she dare ask Sondheim if he would consider restructuring the song with that as the last line? She took another deep breath. He took another look at the song. He agreed. You've never heard the song quite like this before.

PRETTY WOMEN/ THE LADIES WHO LUNCH

When Barbra heard the score from *Sweeney Todd*, she fell in love with "Pretty Women." She knew she had to sing it someday, but she didn't know how, as a woman, she could perform it. Not until she got the idea of "putting it together" with "The Ladies Who Lunch," from *Company*, as its ironic companion piece.

Sondheim, of course, wrote the brilliant additional lyrics for the latter. Peter Matz wrote the exciting arrangement.

Barbra's performance is what theater is all about.

CAN'T HELP LOVIN' THAT MAN

Showboat (1927) occupies a distinguished place in the development of the American musical theater. Preceding it lay the world of operettas and revues with their interchangeable songs, star turns and silly plots. The seeds of the Rodgers and Hammerstein revolution were planted here in Oscar Hammerstein and Jerome Kern's *Showboat*, based on Edna Ferber's novel.

Barbra tried several versions of "Can't Help Lovin' That Man." None felt right to her. None captured that feeling she remembered as a little girl sitting in a dark movie theater in Brooklyn, listening to Ava Gardner sing this song. A search of record stores turned up the original soundtrack album with the Conrad Salinger arrangement. That felt right to her. And that's what she used.

I LOVES YOU PORGY/ PORGY, I'S YOUR WOMAN NOW

(BESS, YOU IS MY WOMAN)

In 1935, George and Ira Gershwin and DuBose Heyward created *Porgy And Bess*. A masterpiece. A synthesis of the classical European tradition and indigenous American music. Folk music. Jazz. It was the forerunner of much of the naturalism we now know on the musical stage. It had real people singing in the operatic idiom.

Barbra has chosen what she feels are "two of the most beautiful melodies ever written." She's been wanting to sing them for years. They've been waiting for her.

SOMEWHERE

In *West Side Story*, "Somewhere" was sung off-stage, commenting on a ballet. Barbra envisioned this song in an electronic setting and asked David Foster to place it in a new environment: space.

There's a glimpse of infinity in it.

—from *The Broadway Album* liner notes

Contents

*With the exception of "Somewhere" and "Something's Coming," all music arrangements were
transcribed directly from the album by Rick Walters.*

PUTTING IT TOGETHER
(From *Sunday in the Park with George*)

Music and Lyrics by
STEPHEN SONDHEIM

Transcribed from the arrangement by Barbra Streisand and Peter Matz.
Mr. Sondheim revised the lyrics for this version of the song, which was recorded by Ms. Streisand.

work.

Art is-n't ea-sy,

E-ven when you're hot.

Ad-

vanc-ing art is ea-sy,

Fi-nanc-ing it is not.

A vi-sion's just a vi-sion if it's on-ly in your head.

If no one gets to hear it, it's as good as dead.

Fast

It has to come to life! _____

_____ Bit by bit,

put - ting it to - geth - er.

get much ex - hi - bi - tion. _____ Art is - n't ea -

- sy, _____ ev - 'ry mi - nor de -

tail is a ma - jor de - ci - sion. Have to keep things in

scale, Have to hold to your vi - sion.

What's a lit - tle cock - tail con - ver - sa - tion If___ it gets the

funds for your foun - da - tion. Ev - 'ry time I start to feel de - fen -

- sive, I___ re - mem - ber vi - nyl is ex - pen - sive!

A lit-tle bit of hype can be ef-fec-tive, Long as you can keep it in per-spec-tive. E-ven when you get some re-cog-ni-tion Ev-'ry-thing you do you still au-di-tion.

Art is-n't ea-sy,

mf

20

And e - ven if it's true, girl,

You do what you can do!

cresc. *f*

Bit by bit, put - ting it to - geth - er.

8va -

shpiel,

Doubt   by   doubt   And   that _____

Is   the   state   of   the   art. _____

f

8va - - - - - - - - - - - - - - - -

IF I LOVED YOU
(From *Carousel*)

Music by RICHARD RODGERS
Lyrics by OSCAR HAMMERSTEIN II

Transcribed from the arrangement by Peter Matz, recorded by Barbra Streisand.

SOMETHING'S COMING
(From *West Side Story*)

Music by LEONARD BERNSTEIN
Lyrics by STEPHEN SONDHEIM

Com - in' to me!

R.H.

f

dim.

Refrain (with rhythmic excitement)

Could it be? Yes, it could
With a click, With a shock.

Some - things's com - ing, Some - thing good,
Phone will jin - gle, Door will knock.

NOT WHILE I'M AROUND

(From *Sweeney Todd*)

Music and Lyrics by
STEPHEN SONDHEIM

Moderately slow, with rubato

Transcribed from the recording by Barbra Streisand.

44

BEING ALIVE
(From *Company*)

Words and Music by
STEPHEN SONDHEIM

Transcribed from the arrangement by Barbra Streisand and Peter Matz, recorded by Ms. Streisand.

I HAVE DREAMED/WE KISS IN A SHADOW/
SOMETHING WONDERFUL
(From *The King and I*)

Words by OSCAR HAMMERSTEIN II
Music by RICHARD RODGERS

Slow and dreamy

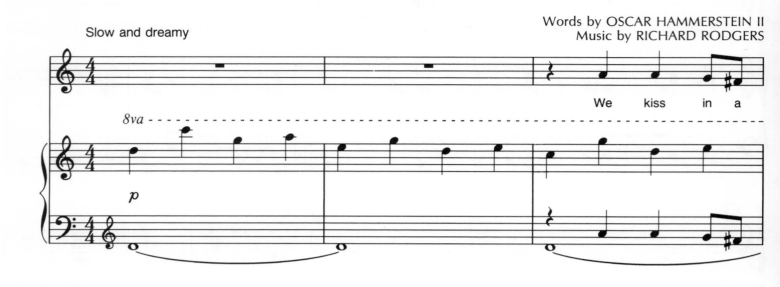

We kiss in a

sha-dow We hide from the moon

Our meet-ings are few and o-ver too soon.

Transcribed from the arrangement by Bob Esty and Paul Jabara, recorded by Barbra Streisand.

54

SEND IN THE CLOWNS
(From *A Little Night Music*)

Music and Lyrics by
STEPHEN SONDHEIM

This arrangement includes Mr. Sondheim's revised lyrics for Barbra Streisand's recording.

61

CAN'T HELP LOVIN' THAT MAN

(CAN'T HELP LOVIN' DAT MAN)
(From *Showboat*)

Words by OSCAR HAMMERSTEIN II
Music by JEROME KERN

Transcribed from the arrangement by Conrad Salinger and Peter Matz, recorded by Barbra Streisand.

65

67

PRETTY WOMEN/
(From *Sweeney Todd*)
THE LADIES WHO LUNCH
(From *Company*)

Music and Lyrics by
STEPHEN SONDHEIM

Transcribed from the arrangement by Barbra Streisand and Peter Matz, recorded by Ms. Streisand.

74

I LOVES YOU PORGY/
PORGY, I'S YOUR WOMAN NOW
(Bess, You Is My Woman) (From *Porgy and Bess*)

Music by GEORGE GERSHWIN
Lyrics by IRA GERSHWIN, DUBOSE HEYWARD

Moderately and Freely

Transcribed from the arrangement by Barbra Streisand and Peter Matz, recorded by Ms. Streisand.

84

SOMEWHERE
(From *West Side Story*)

Music by LEONARD BERNSTEIN
Lyrics by STEPHEN SONDHEIM